楊文標 • **Violin Pieces**

Per tutte le tue canzoni

C o n t e n t s

楊文標 · Violin Pieces——Per tutte le tue canzoni
作　　者／楊文標
標題設計／楊嘉會
企　　畫／楊禹文
主　　編／洪雅雯
封面設計／盧美瑾
美術設計／盧美瑾
企劃製作／楊文標才能教育工作室
　　　　　http://blog.yam.com/piao0108
　　　　　E-mail: cathy_yang2002@yahoo.com.tw
　　　　　台北市111士林德行西路47-1號3樓
　　　　　電話：02-2833-5107；0913-343-000

發 行 所／台北市中華路一段59號8樓之1
出 版 者／晴易文坊媒體行銷有限公司
製版印刷／
初版一刷／2010年4月10日
定　　價／450元（如有缺頁或破損請寄回更換）

Printed in Taiwan

楊　文標

Ha-ir asher badad yoshevet U-ve-libbah homah.
Forse che io non sono un violino per tutte le tue canzoni.
Schaut her: ich bin eine Geige für alle eure Lieder.
Behold I am a violin for all your songs.

1934 年生於台灣台北市，淡江英語專科學校（淡江大學前身）畢業，12歲開始習琴，後師事於司徒興城。1959年7月4日晚假台北市國際學舍舉行生平首次獨奏會，廣獲好評。先後曾任東吳大學絃樂團老師、淡水工商絃樂團指導老師、成功高中絃樂團指導老師等等。從40年前開始推廣兒童音樂教育，致力在「音樂才能教育」領域，近年來陸續將數十年來推廣兒童音樂的材料、所得整理集結成冊。楊文標老師繼作品《Caprices綺想曲 台灣民謠》將精選台灣民謠改編成小提琴曲，曲譜中融合各種小提琴技巧與弓法，曲韻上蘊含早期台灣民謠的真意，通俗的曲目、貼切的詮釋，深獲各界好評。

2010年，春，推出《楊文標・Violin Pieces Per tutte le tue canzoni》。

【著作】

1971年 9月《才能教育雜誌》刊物
2007年 3月《楊文標才能教育指導曲集1》
2007年10月《楊文標才能教育指導曲集2》
2008年2月《Caprices綺想曲 台灣民謠》
2010年3月《楊文標・Violin Pieces——Per tutte le tue canzoni》

1 Finding Dragonfly

Brilliant concert arrangement for soloists of the virtuoso type.
Violin Alone
問田嬰(蜻蜓)

Jih Shwu-ling
紀淑玲
Arr.1998.8.1

2 Serenade

Schubert
Arr. Wagahai Yang

3 Schon Rosmarin

Kreisler
Revised and Fingered
by Wagahai Yang

4 Menuett

Dussek

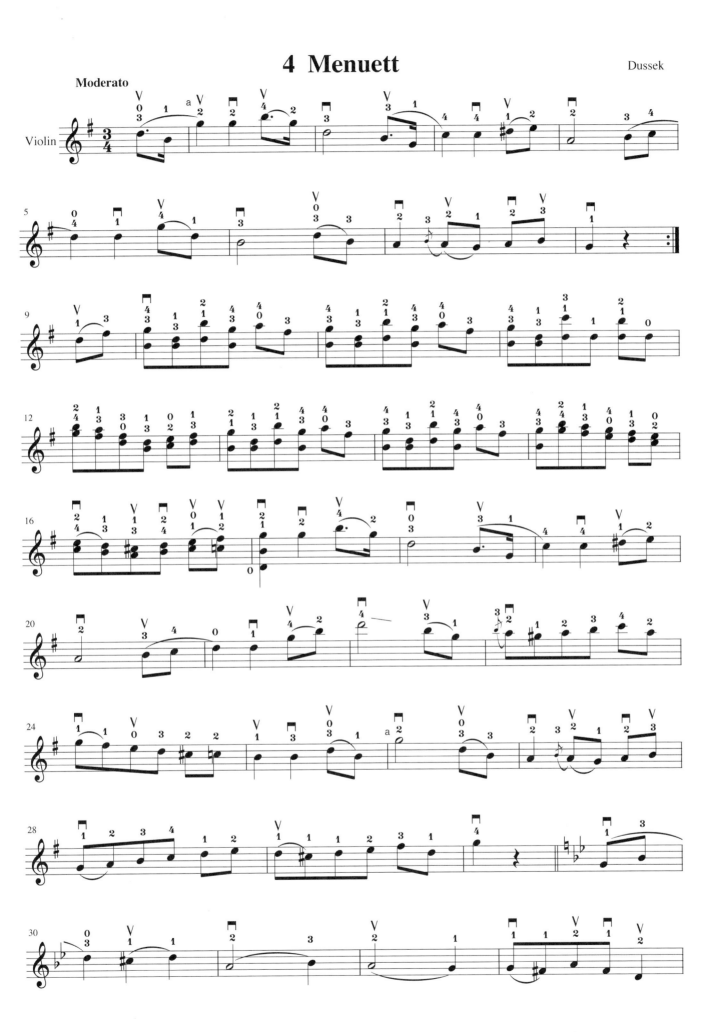

5 Valse

Volkslied
Arr. Wagahai Yang

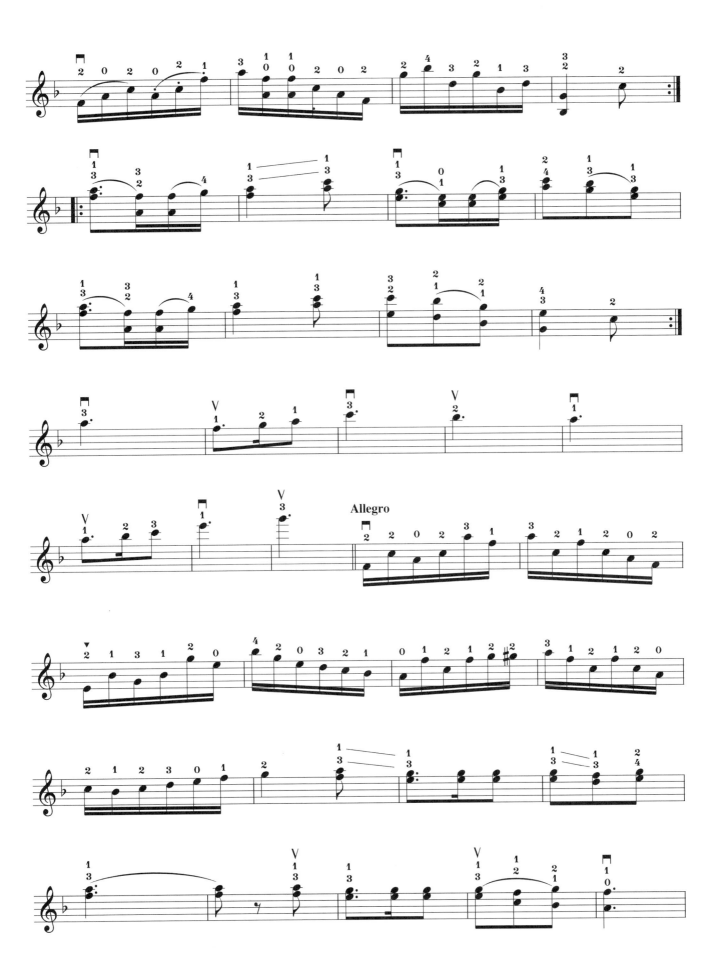

21

6 csardas no no

Nagy Zoltan

Violin

7 Hamabe no uta

Narita tame zuo

8 L'Elisir D'Amore

Una furtiva lagrima

Donizetti
Arr.1989.7.18

9 The Harebell

W. Smallwood
Arr.Wagahai Yang

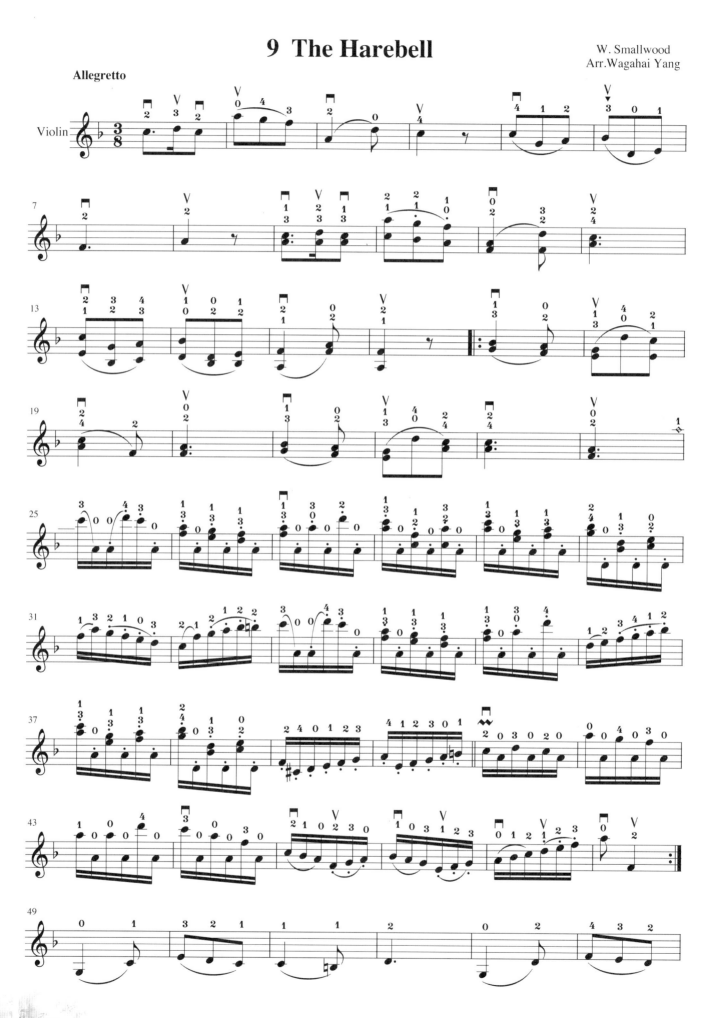

10 Hora Staccato

(1908)

G.Dinicu (1889-1949)

33

11 souper csadas

Zoltan

Allegro assai

12 Fifth Nocturne

Leybach
Arr. Wagahai Yang 1989.5.30

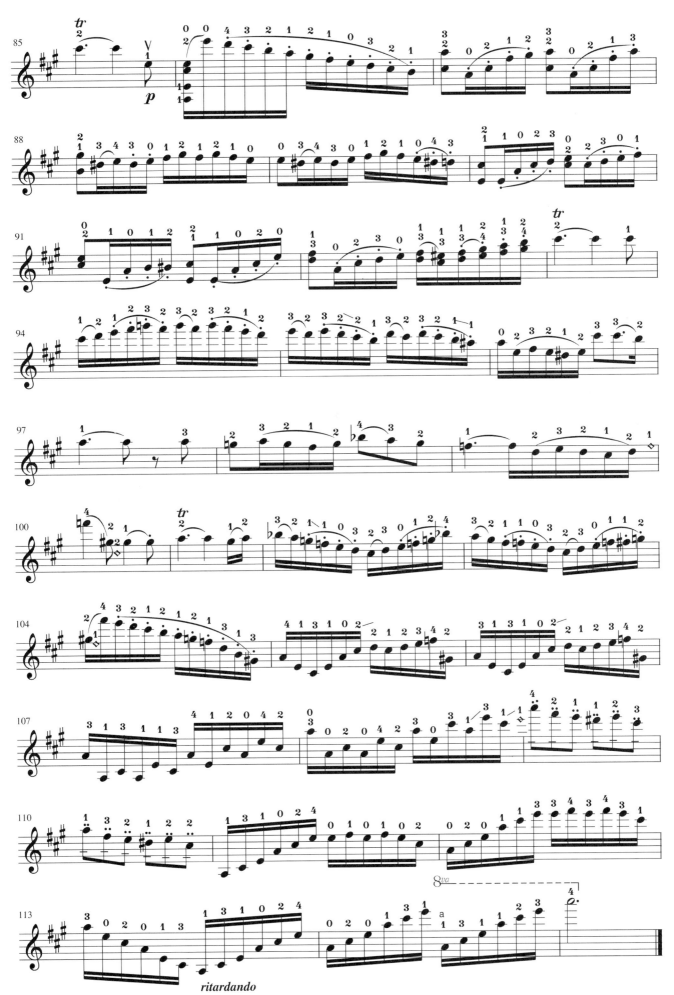

13 Danza delle spade

Khatchaturian

14 Il Barbiere di Siviglia

Largo al factotum della citta

Rossini
Arr. Wagahai Yang 1989.7.21

15 Romanian Rhapsody

No.1 Op.11.in A (1901)

George Enescu (1881-1955)
arr. Wagahai Yang
2009.08.28.

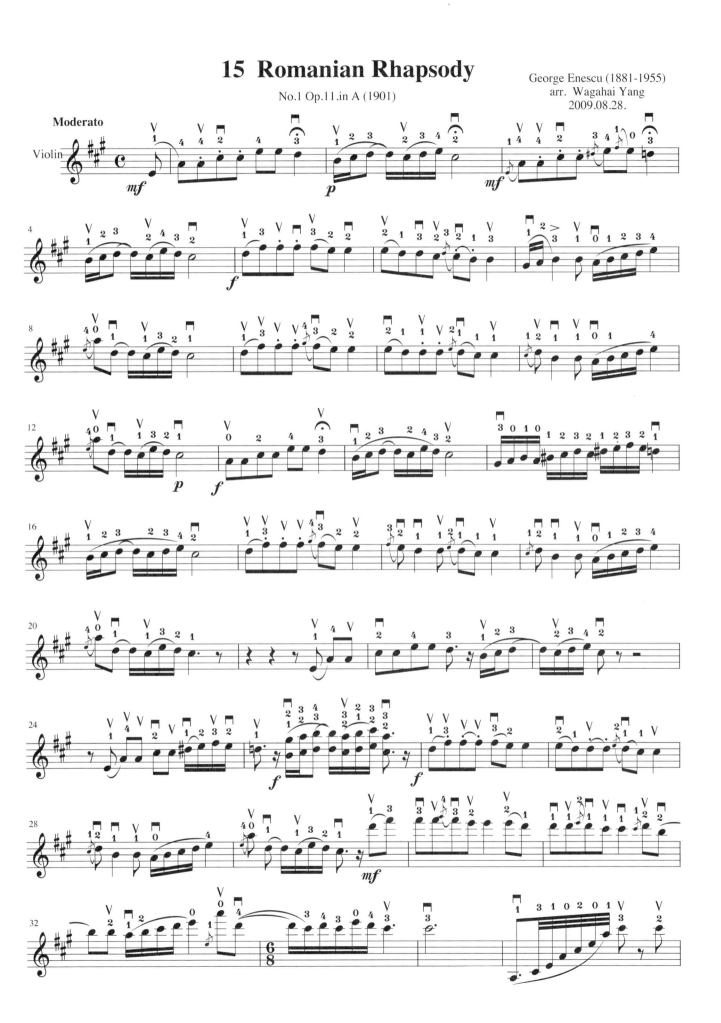

16 Caprice in G major

On the Theme "Taiwan Folksong"
Brilliant concert arrangement for soloists of the virtuoso type.
Violin alone

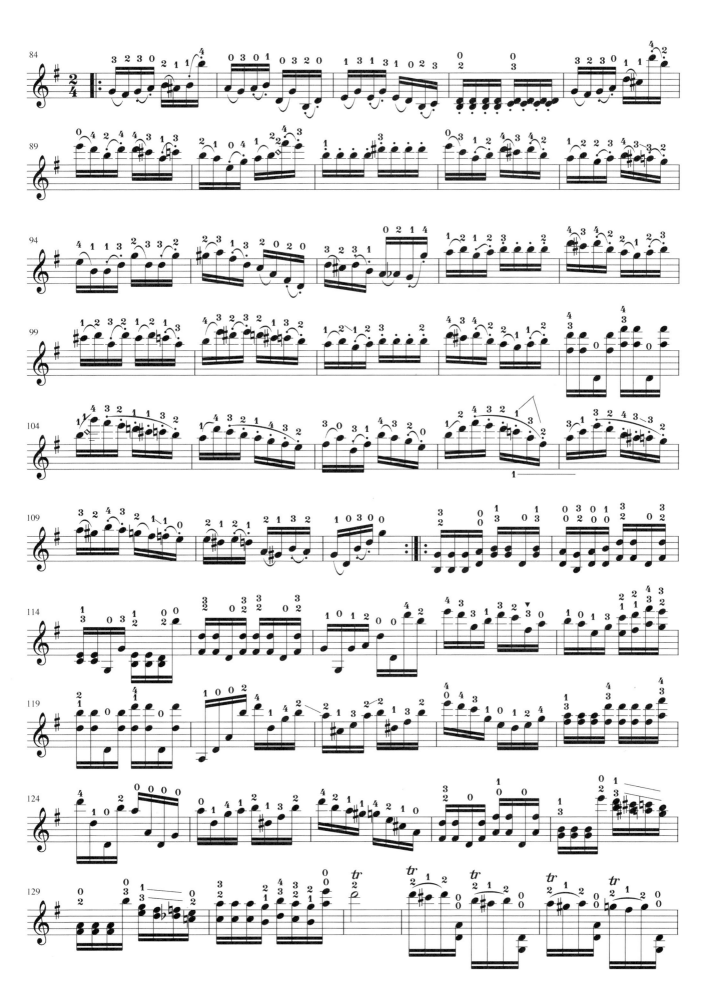

17 Caprice in e minor

On the Theme "Taiwan Folksong"
Brilliant concert arrangement for soloists of the virtuoso type.
Violin alone

Arr. Wagahai Yang

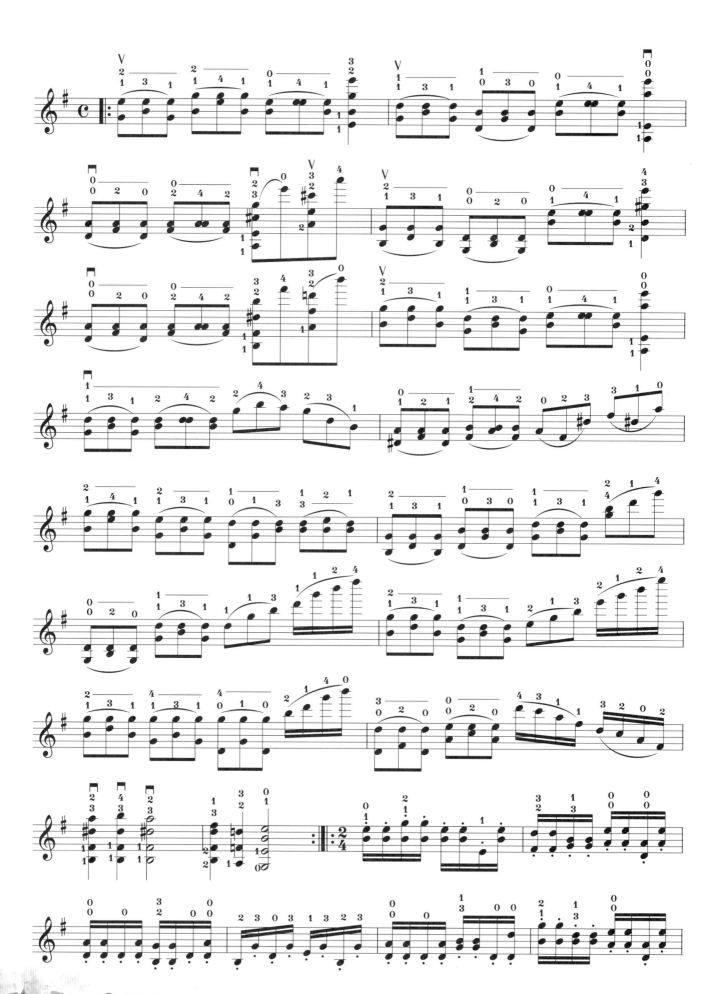

18 Caprice in a minor

On the Theme "Taiwan Folksong"

Violin alone

Arr. Wagahai Yang

19 Caprice in D major

Violin alone

Arr. Wagahai Yang

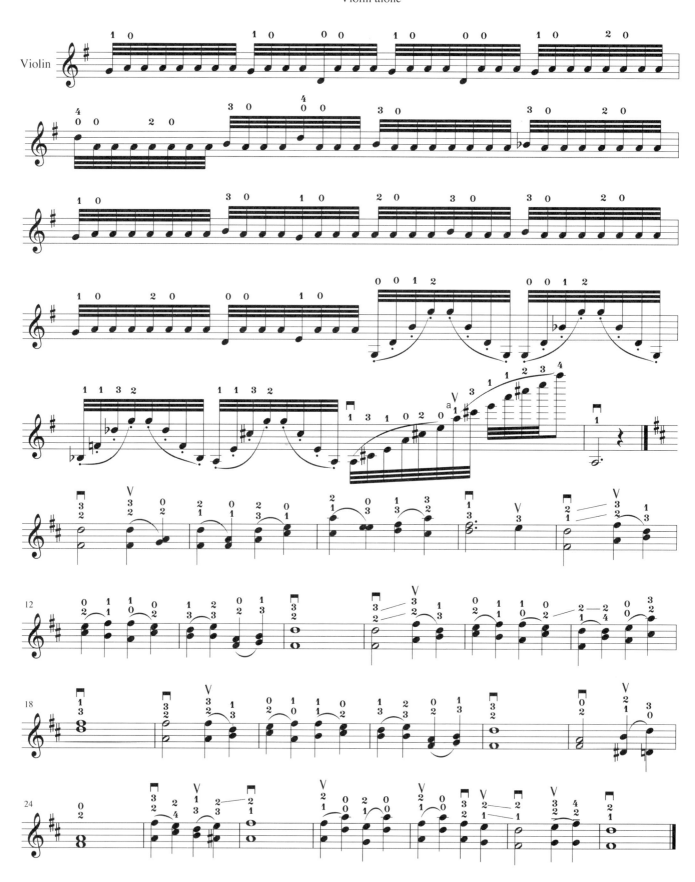

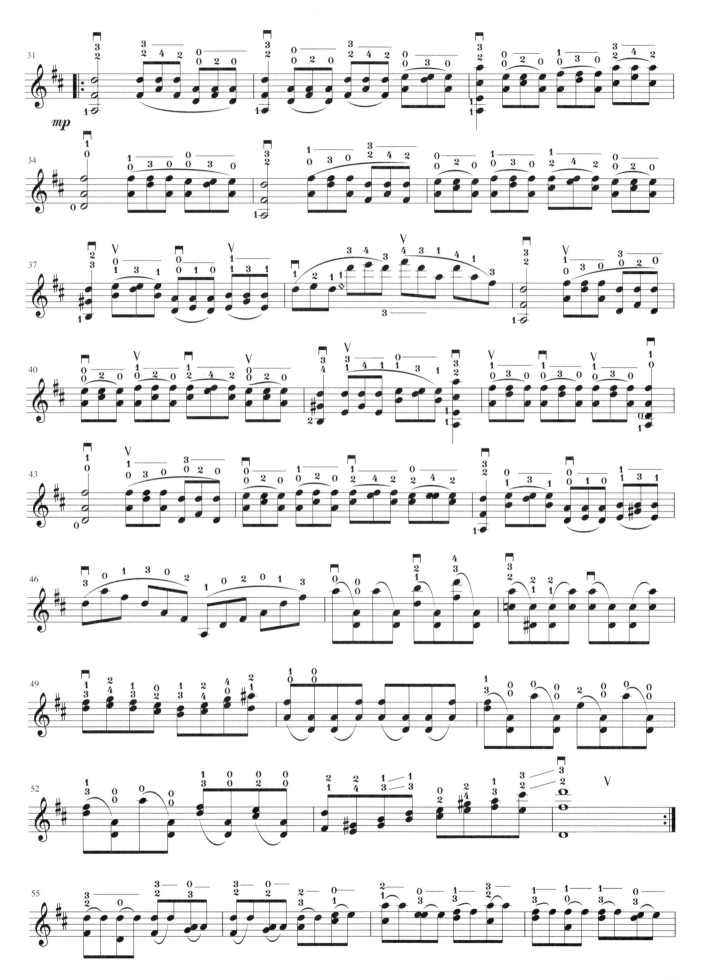

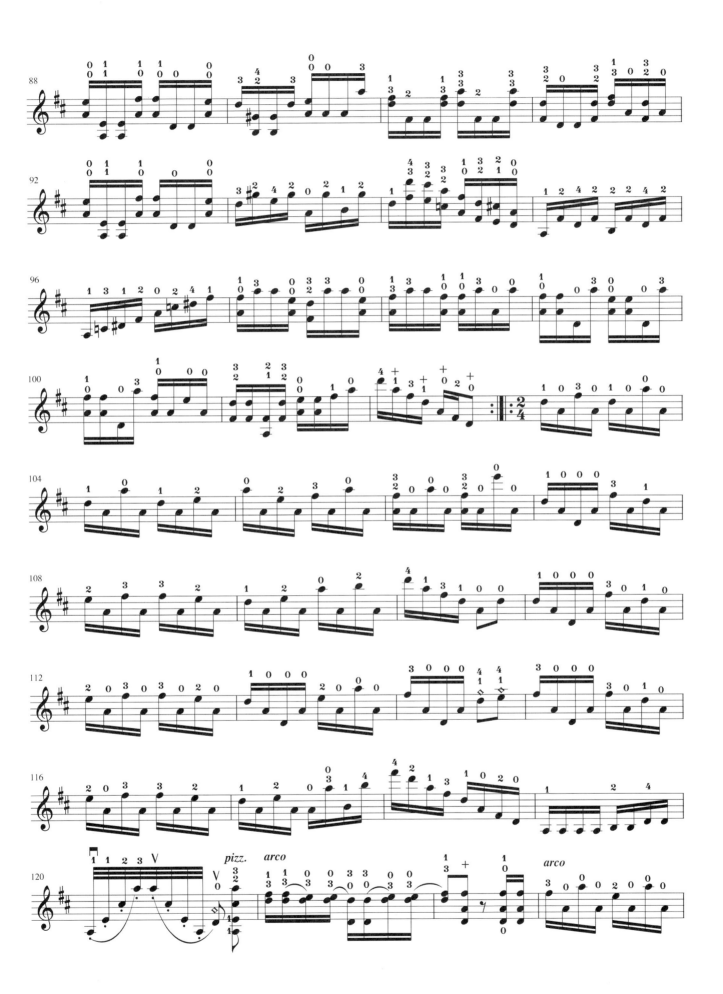

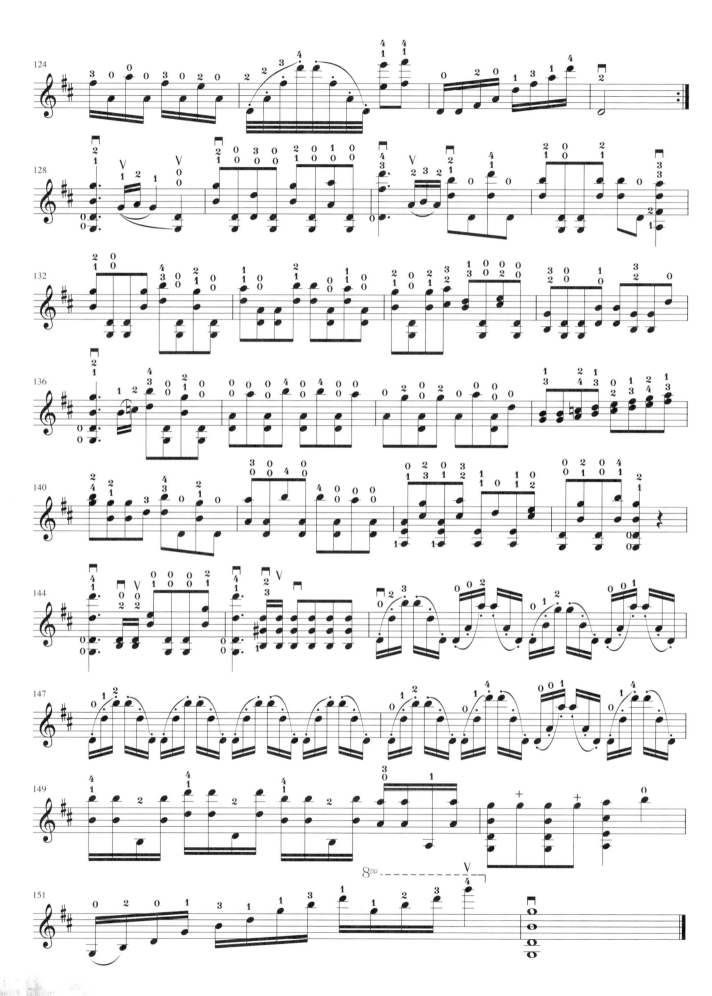

20 Cadenza

Mozart Violin Concerto No.3 1st. mov.

by Wagahai Yang
06.09.1989